How Pirates Really Work!

by Alan Snow

SIMON AND SCHUSTER
London   Aberdeenshire   New Delhi

And So My Story Begins . . .

It all began some threescore years ago in a small town in the West. I lived with my mother and twenty-six brothers and sisters in a tiny cottage. There was always a lot happening in our busy little town and I would spend all my time down at the harbour watching what went on. I never grew tired of seeing the fishing boats and merchant ships come and go with all their varied cargoes.

The sailors sang hearty songs and would sometimes throw a small part of the
day's catch or some other titbit my way. I always wondered what it might be
like to live out on the open seas, rolling in the deep.
One night, I noticed a ship arrive very quietly. I watched as the crew
tied up and made their way to the pub. I crept along behind them.
After seeing how jolly they were, I decided to stow away and
go to sea with them.

Setting Sail

I hid below deck between two cannons, thinking that the crew wouldn't be using those at so early a stage of the journey. Soon I felt the ship begin to roll and dip and realised we had left the harbour. We were off!

I poked my head out from my hiding place and heard a shout of, 'Brazil! Look out! The best crew that ever there was is coming your way!' Brazil. I had heard the men speaking of it at the docks and knew that meant we sailed in search of gold. The ultimate booty! I could not have been more excited.

It wasn't long before I was discovered by the crew. At first they were angry, but they soon found plenty of use for me. First task: get to know the ship from top to bottom.

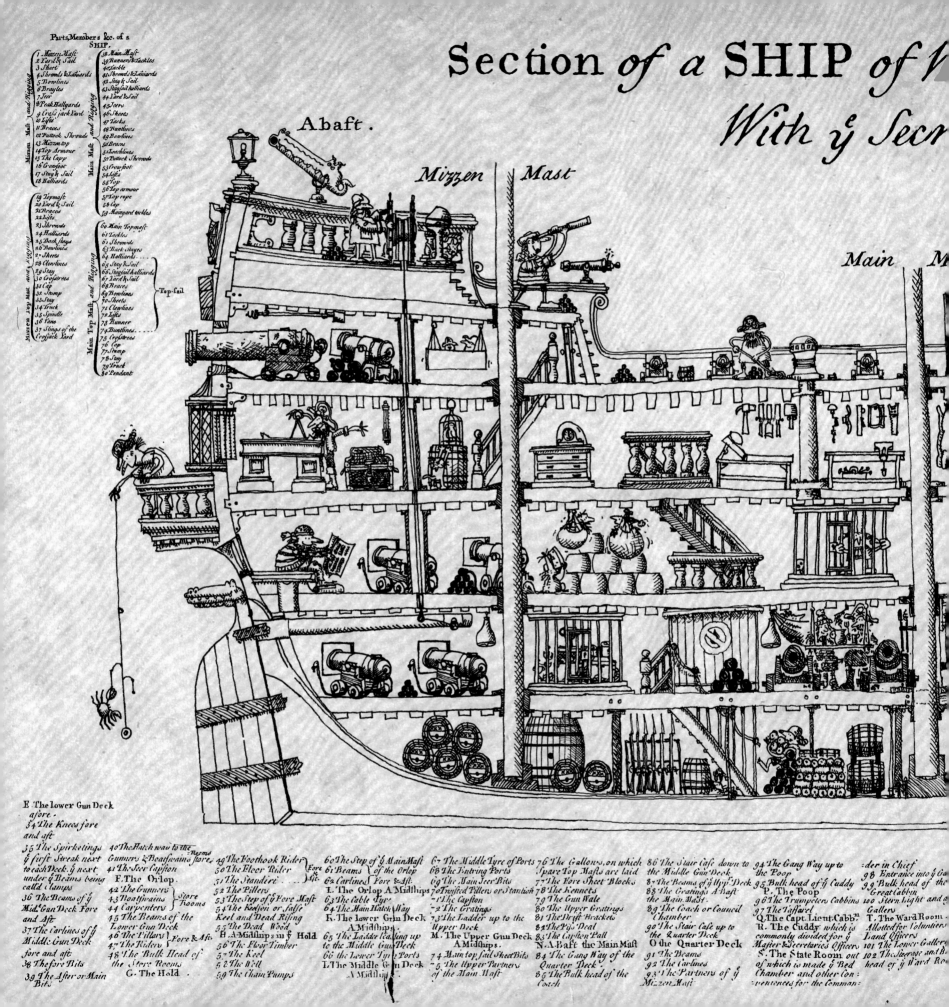

Section of a SHIP of W...

With ẙ Secr...

Abaft.

Mizzen Mast

Main M...

Parts, Members &c. of a
SHIP.

1 Mizzen Mast
2 Yard & Sail
3 Sheet
4 Shrouds & Lattiards
5 Bowlines
6 Brayles
7 Jeer
8 Peak Hallyards
9 Cross jack Yard
10 Lifts
11 Braces
12 Puttock Shrouds
13 Mizzen top
14 Top Armour
15 The Capp
16 Crosfoot
17 Stay & Sail
18 Halliards

19 Topmast
20 Yard & Sail
21 Braces
22 Lifts
23 Shrowds
24 Halliards
25 Back stays
26 Bowlines
27 Sheets
28 Clewlines
29 Stay
30 Crosstrees
31 Cap
32 Stump
33 Stay
34 Truck
35 Spindle
36 Fans
37 Slings of the Crossjack Yard

38 Main Mast
39 Yard & Sail
40 Tackle
41 Shrouds & Lattiards
42 Stay & Sail
43 Stay sail halliards
44 Yard & Sail
45 Jeers
46 Sheets
47 Tacks
48 Buntlines
49 Bowlines
50 Braces
51 Leechlines
52 Puttock Shrouds
53 Crowfoot
54 Lifts
55 Top
56 Top armour
57 Top rope
58 Cap
59 Mainyard tackles

60 Main Topmast
61 Tackles
62 Shrowds
63 Back stayes
64 Halliards
65 Stay & Sail
66 Stayfail halliards
67 Yard & Sail
68 Braces
69 Bowlines
70 Sheets
71 Clewlines
72 Lifts
73 Runner
74 Buntlines
75 Crosstrees
76 Cap
77 Stump
78 Stay
79 Truck
80 Pendant

Mizzen Mast and Rigging
Main Mast and Rigging
Mizzen Top Mast and Rigging
Main Top Mast and Rigging
Top-Sail

E The lower Gun Deck
afore

34 The Knees fore
and aft

35 The Spirketings
ẙ first Streak next
to each Deck ẙ next
under ẙ Beams being
call'd Clamps

36 The Beams of ẙ
Mid.t Gun Deck Fore
and Aft

37 The Carlines of ẙ
Middle Gun Deck
fore and aft

38 The fore Bits

39 The After or Main
Bits

40 The Hatch way to the
Gunners & Boatswains store
41 The Jeer Capston
F. The Orlop
42 The Gunners
43 Boatswains
44 Carpenters
45 The Beams of the
Lower Gun Deck
46 The Pillars
47 The Riders
48 The Bulk Head of
the Store Rooms
G. The Hold.

Rooms
Store Rooms
Fore & Aft

49 The Foothook Rider
50 The Floor Rider
51 The Standers
52 The Pillers
53 The Step of ẙ Fore Mast
54 The Kelson or false
Keel and Dead Rising
55 The Dead Wood
H. A Midships in ẙ Hold
65 The Ladder leading up
to the Middle Gun Deck
56 The Floor Timber
57 The Well
58 The Chain Pumps
59 The Chain Pumps

60 The Step of ẙ Main Mast
61 Beams of the Orlop
62 Carlines Fore & Aft
I. The Orlop A Midships
63 The Cable Tyr
64 The Main Hatch Way
K. The lower Gun Deck
65 The Ladder up to the
Upper Deck
66 the Lower Tyre Ports
L. The Middle Gun Deck
A Midships

Fore
Aft

67 The Middle Tyre of Ports
68 The Entring Ports
69 The Main Jeer Bits
70 Trussed Pillers or Stantion
1 The Capston
2 The Gratings
73 The Ladder up to the
Upper Deck
M. The Upper Gun Deck
A Midships
74 Main top Sail Sheet Bits
5 The Upper Partners
of the Main Mast

76 The Gallows, on which
Spare Top Masts are laid
77 The Fore Sheet Blocks
78 The Kennets
79 The Gun Wale
80 The Upper Gratings
81 The Drift Brackets
82 The Pifs Deal
83 The Capston Pall
N. A Baft the Main Mast
84 The Gang Way of the
Quarter Deck
85 The Bulk head of the
Coach

86 The Stair Case down to
the Middle Gun Deck
87 The Beams of ẙ Uppr Deck
88 The Gratings A baft
the Main Mast
89 The Coach or Council
Chamber
90 The Stair Case up to
the Quarter Deck
O the Quarter Deck
91 The Beams
92 The Carlines
93 The Partners of ẙ
Mizzen Mast

94 The Gang Way up to
the Poop
95 Bulk head of ẙ Cuddy
P. The Poop
96 The Trumpeters Cabbins
97 The Taffarel
Q. The Capt. Lieut. Cabb.n
R. The Cuddy which is
commonly divided for ẙ
Master & Secretaries Officers
S. The State Room out
of which is made ẙ Bed
Chamber and other Con-
veniences for the Comman-

...der in Chief
98 Entrance into ẙ Coa...
99 Bulk head of the
Great Cabbin
100 Stern Light and a...
Gallery
T. The Ward Room
101 The Lower Galler...
102 The Steerage and B...
head of ẙ Ward Roo...

l ships   Afore.

Fore | Mast

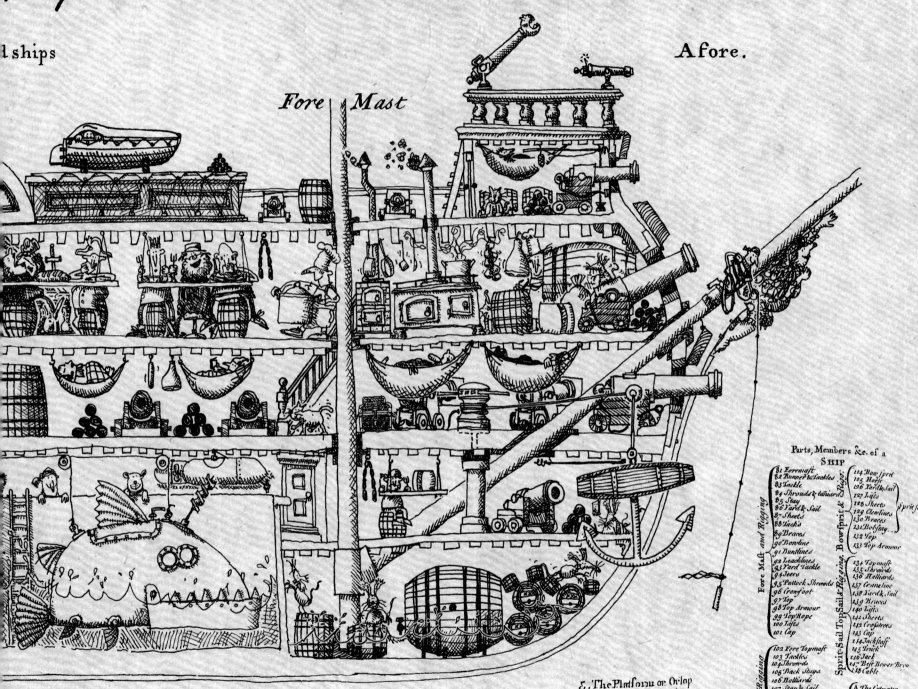

Parts, Members &c. of a
SHIP

Fore Mast and Rigging	Sprit-Sail Top Sail & Rigging	Bowsprit & Rigging
81 Foremast	114 Bow sprit	
82 Runner & Tackles	125 Horse	
83 Tackle	126 Yard & Sail	
84 Shrouds & tawards	127 Lifts	
85 Stay	128 Sheets	
86 Yard & Sail	129 Clewlines	Sprit sail
87 Sheets	130 Braces	
88 Jack's	131 Bolt stay	
89 Braces	132 Top	
90 Bowline	133 Top Armour	
91 Buntlines		
92 Leachlines	134 Topmast	
93 Yard Tackle	135 Shrouds	
94 Jeers	136 Halliards	
95 Puttock Shrouds	137 Craneline	
96 Cronfoot	138 Yard & Sail	
97 Top	139 Braces	
98 Top Armour	140 Lifts	
99 Top Rope	141 Sheets	
100 Lifts	142 Crosstrees	
101 Cap	143 Cap	
	144 Jackstaff	
102 Fore Topmast	145 Truck	
103 Tackles	146 Jack	
104 Shrouds	147 Best Bower Bow	
105 Back Stays	148 Cable	
106 Halliards		
107 Stay & Sail		
108 Halliards		
109 Yard & Sail		
110 Runner		
111 Lifts		
112 Braces		
113 Sheets		
114 Clewlines		
115 Bundlines		
116 Crosstrees		
117 Crosstrees		
118 Cap		
119 Stump		
120 Stay		
121 Truck		
122 Spindle		
123 Fane		

Fore Top Mast and Rigging

Hull:
A The Cutwater
B Stem
C Hasholes
D Cathead
E Wastecloths
F Fore Channel
G Main Channel
H Mizzen'hannel
I Chestree
K Entring Port
L Head
M Gallery
N Taffarell
O Poop Lanthorns
P Ensign Staff
Q Truck
R Ensign

Parts, Members &c. Within side
103 The Whipstaff comanding
the Tillar.
104 The After Stair Case
down to ỷ lower Gun Deck
V. Several Officers Cabins
A baft ỷ Main Mast in which

Place comonly the Soldier
Make their Guard from the
Entring Port.
W. The Gun Room.
105 The Tillar comanding the
Rudder
106 The Rudder
107 The Stern Post
108 The Tillar Transom

109 The several Transoms &c.
1.2.3.4.5
110 The Gun Room Port or
Stern Chase
111 Bread Room Scuttle
down out of the Gun Room
112 The main Capston
113 The Pall of the Capston
or Stopper of Iron
114 The Partners

X. The Bread Room
115 The Bulk Head of the
Bread Room
Y. The Stewards Room
Where all Provisions are
weighed and Served out
Z. The Cock Pit where
are Subdivisions for the
Purser and Chirurgeons &
Mates

E. The Platform or Orlop
where Provision is made in
time of Service for the wounds
116 The Hold abaft the
Main Mast
117 Step of ỷ Mizzen
Mast
118 The Keelson or Falfe
Keel
119 Dead Wood or Rising

A DAY IN THE LIFE OF A PIRATE

The time on a ship is divided into four hour 'watches'. Sailors have to work a pattern of four hours on, four hours off. This goes right through the night.

1. GET UP AT 7 AM

Morning already?!

2. WASH AND DRESS

5. LOOKOUT DUTY FROM CROW'S NEST

Water, water everywhere and not a drop to drink!

6. BREAK FOR SHIP'S BISCUITS
Break teeth, more like!

Remind me why we do this every day again?

7. PRACTISE BALANCING 15 MEN ON A DEAD MAN'S CHEST

10. MORE SWABBING THE DECKS

11. LUNCH

14. CANNON PRACTICE

15. SINGING PRACTICE

Pirate Skills!

There are lots of things a trainee pirate needs to learn. It's a long way from Dorset to Brazil, so you get plenty of chance to brush up your new skills.

If we use a magnet we can make North any way we want!

NAVIGATION

First you have to learn to use a compass and a map, then work out the speed of the boat. There is an instrument called a sextant that's used to measure the height of the sun, and knowing this and the exact time, helps to work out where you are.

This is a sextant. Be very careful not to poke it in your eye or look directly into the sun.

SINGING. A good skill for all pirates.

When we work together we might have to keep in time and at other times it helps keep us jolly.

Row, row, row your boat gently down the stream , , ,

BOAT HANDLING. Without lots of practice it's almost impossible to sail a boat. But once you know how to, it can really help. Not only in everyday sailing but also when you are in a battle and need to use tactics.

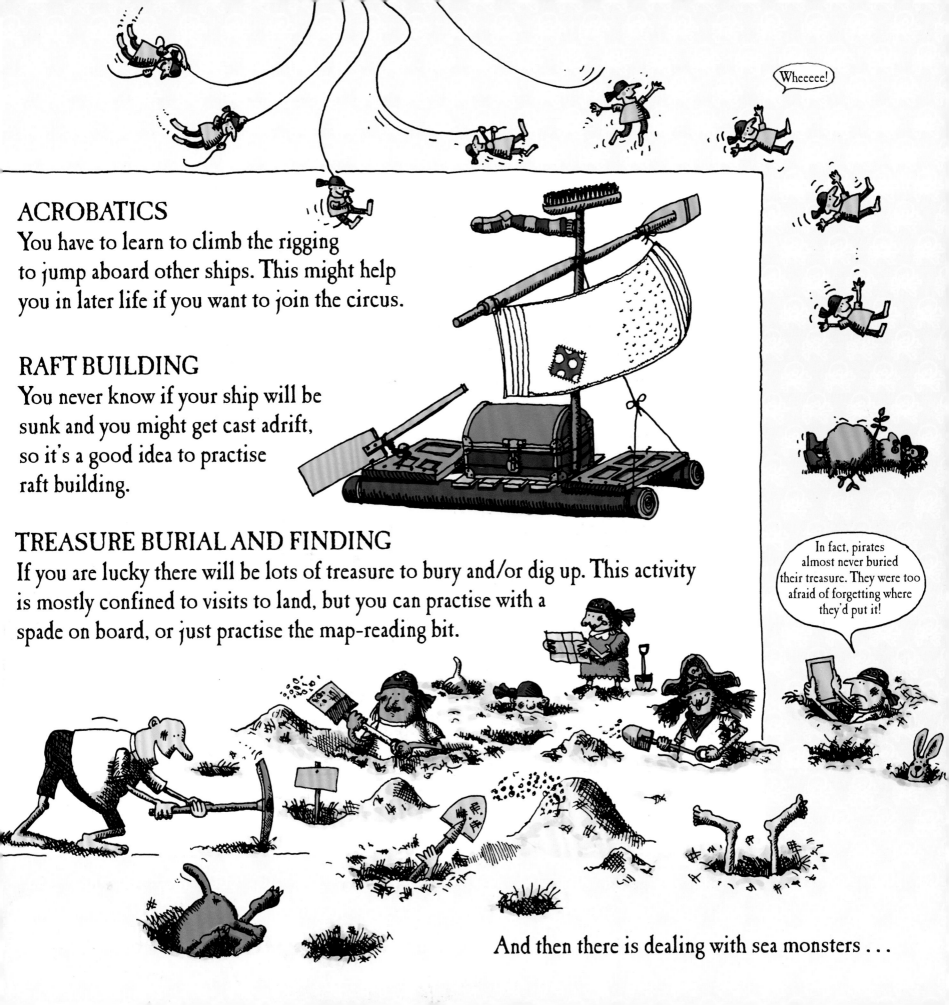

ACROBATICS

You have to learn to climb the rigging
to jump aboard other ships. This might help
you in later life if you want to join the circus.

RAFT BUILDING

You never know if your ship will be
sunk and you might get cast adrift,
so it's a good idea to practise
raft building.

TREASURE BURIAL AND FINDING

If you are lucky there will be lots of treasure to bury and/or dig up. This activity
is mostly confined to visits to land, but you can practise with a
spade on board, or just practise the map-reading bit.

Wheeeee!

In fact, pirates
almost never buried
their treasure. They were too
afraid of forgetting where
they'd put it!

And then there is dealing with sea monsters . . .

SEVEN-HEADED HYDRA

SOLUTION: the new improved umbrella fishing rod attachment.

SEA SERPENT

SOLUTION: a large twisted tube and bait to lure it through until it ties itself in a knot.

JAPANESE EARTHQUAKE-CAUSING CATFISH

SOLUTION: extra-large exploding mouse.

PARROTS!

People think pirates all have parrots. We don't! We hate parrots. They bite, talk and give away where you hide treasure and keep you up at all times of day and night with their squawking. Not only that but they get washed overboard. As we are expected to have parrots we have to have a way around this, and the answer is DIY parrots and a little bit of ventriloquism. What's more if you use a hook to act as a hand, you can operate the parrot and no one will guess.

HOW TO MAKE A PIRATE PARROT

1. Use three old socks, one for the body and head, and the other two for wings.

2. Use buttons for eyes but do try to find evil buttons to give the right effect.

3. A beak can be made of cardboard. This should be painted in a bright colour with waterproof paint as it is likely to get wet in storms.

4. You then have to learn ventriloquism (talking without moving your lips). False beards are useful for this.

What is orange and sounds like a parrot?

A carrot.

GROG + GRUB

If you like your food, you're in for a rough time at sea. Stored food goes off and even the water goes foul. After the first few weeks the only safe foods left are things that can be pickled, dried or preserved. If you're very lucky there might be fresh meat, eggs and milk from animals kept on board. Everything else goes rotten and mouldy. It's not healthy and lots of pirates got a disease called scurvy before it was discovered that lemons or pickled cabbage would stop you getting sick and all your teeth falling out.

Ship's biscuits are so hard you could use them to knock in nails! They are called 'hardtack' and are part of every meal, worse luck. We soak them to make them softer, but even then they are usually still wriggling with worms. Yuck!

A real treat is turtles and giant tortoises. They are really scrummy. (Although the shell is a bit too crunchy for my taste.) Dodos are also good to eat. A bit too good, unfortunately, and now they are all extinct!

Why are pirates the best?

Because they arrrrrr!

Treasure & Booty!

So you have got some treasure (or booty as it's known). What do you do with it?

Someone could come and steal it from you so it's best to hide it so only you and your crew can find it. The best thing is to bury it on an island where no one lives (that is why you did all the digging practice!) But you also have to make a map so you can find it again. But just in case the map falls into the wrong hands, it's best to use a code or clever clues to tell you where the treasure is buried so only you will know where it is. (In fact only one pirate, William Kidd, is known to have buried his booty.)

Many people think that we pirates are only interested in gold and silver in big wooden chests. And we do love all that, who wouldn't?

But there are plenty of other kinds of treasure that we value too. You might be surprised to discover that tea is very precious to us. We can do a roaring trade in the makings of a good cuppa so if we spot a ship coming home from China or India then we'll set our sights on it quick-sharp. And if you like a spoonful of sugar in your brew, then so do we, and any ships carrying sugar back from the Caribbean can expect a little visit from us too!

We are also always very glad to get our hands on cotton, spices, soap and even frying pans. We're not fussy!

What do you call a pirate who has lost his spade? Douglas.

What do you call a pirate with a spade? Doug.

Equipment & Weapons

Fearsome weapons for fearless pirates.

The cannon is the common name for this type of weapon, but each size used to have its own name.

POLE CANNON

SWIVEL GUN

DRAGON GUN

CANNONADE

LONG GUN

MORTAR

Even though we pirates are very brave, we do all we can to avoid actual fighting and instead like to put on a show to scare our enemies. If it does come to a fight, we use clever tactics so we don't damage the ships we want to take over.

THE CANNON

Botefeux

Cannonball

Rammer

Touch hole

Charge

Wad screw

Cannons were thicker and stronger where the explosion took place and thinner at the end of the barrel.

We do use cannonballs, but also use different types of shot that damage an enemy ship but don't sink it.

GUNPOWDER CHARGE
A fast and safe way to handle gunpowder. The charges were stored in the magazine deep in the ship and brought up to the gun deck when needed.

CANNONBALLS
Good for sinking ships, and stored in racks or stands called brass monkeys.

CHAIN SHOT AND BAR SHOT
Take down sails and rigging.

CANNON GRENADES
Exploding bombs shot from the cannon.

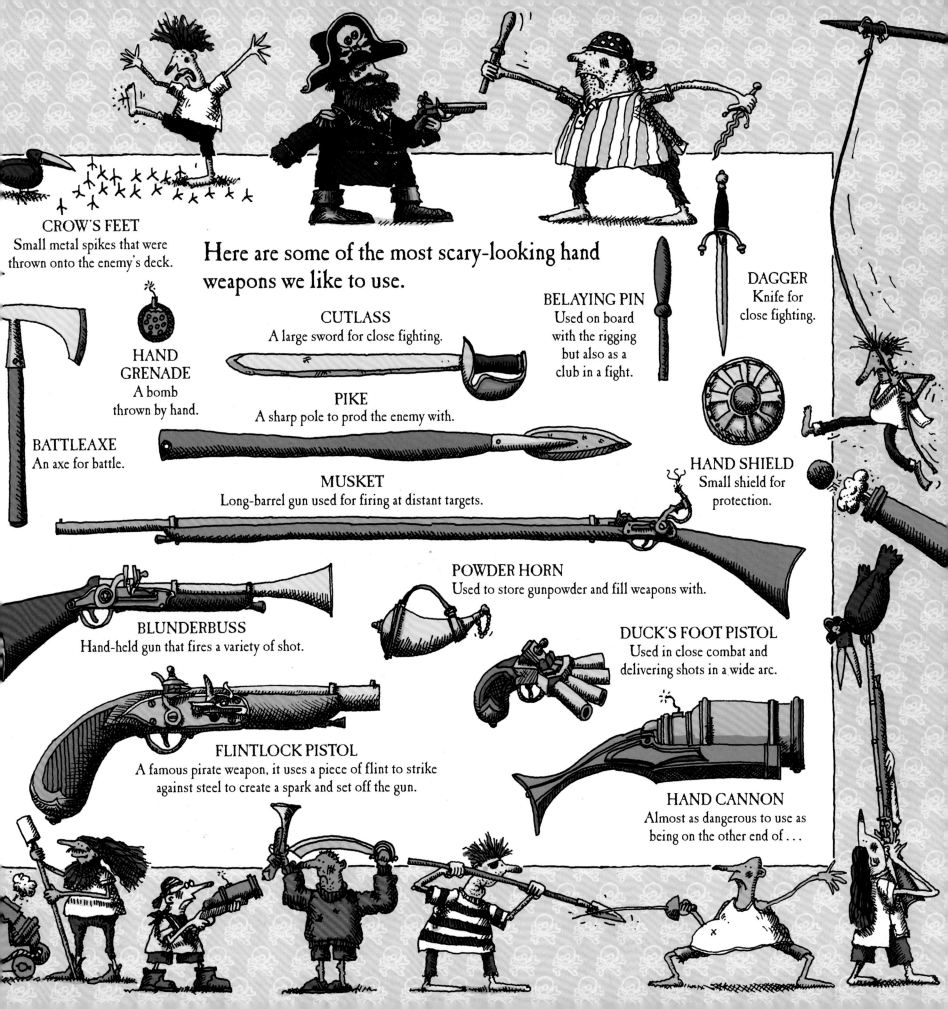

CROW'S FEET
Small metal spikes that were thrown onto the enemy's deck.

Here are some of the most scary-looking hand weapons we like to use.

HAND GRENADE
A bomb thrown by hand.

CUTLASS
A large sword for close fighting.

PIKE
A sharp pole to prod the enemy with.

BELAYING PIN
Used on board with the rigging but also as a club in a fight.

DAGGER
Knife for close fighting.

BATTLEAXE
An axe for battle.

MUSKET
Long-barrel gun used for firing at distant targets.

HAND SHIELD
Small shield for protection.

BLUNDERBUSS
Hand-held gun that fires a variety of shot.

POWDER HORN
Used to store gunpowder and fill weapons with.

DUCK'S FOOT PISTOL
Used in close combat and delivering shots in a wide arc.

FLINTLOCK PISTOL
A famous pirate weapon, it uses a piece of flint to strike against steel to create a spark and set off the gun.

HAND CANNON
Almost as dangerous to use as being on the other end of . . .

FAMOUS PIRATES

Ching Shih, a woman and one of the most successful pirates of all time, had a short career, taking early retirement when the government offered her the chance of an amnesty. She was undefeated by the British, Portuguese and Chinese and had a fleet of as many as 1500 ships.

Bartholomew Roberts was a very successful Welsh pirate who 'worked' the Caribbean. He had rules on his ships. For example, each man shall have equal vote, food and drink. Lights out at 8pm and no music on Sundays.

Blackbeard's real name was William Teach. He was famous for wearing flaming tapers in his beard. He died in a fierce battle with a force of Americans, sent to hunt him down.

Ann Bonnie married Calico Jack Rackham while on board his ship. She would fight and take on other duties as much as any other crew member. She and her husband were captured. Her husband was hanged, but she disappeared – some think her father paid a ransom to have her freed.

Clock Eaten by Crocodile

Capt. Morgan

Captain Hook was a fictional pirate, and appears in Peter Pan by J M Barrie. He lost his hand to Peter Pan, which was then eaten by a crocodile! The crocodile went on to eat a clock.

Captain Henry Morgan was a Welsh pirate who spent a lot of his time in the West Indies. He was given missions by the Governor of Jamaica to attack the Spanish and Dutch in the area. These missions were to gain riches for himself and the Governor, using the excuse of protecting Jamaica and the British interest. He probably died of a mix of too much drink and 'the dropsy'.

Jacquette Delahaye was a woman pirate from Haiti. She sailed the seas and robbed many but when she found herself too famous, she faked her own death and lived as a man for many years. When she returned as herself, she became known as 'Back from the Dead Red' because she had red hair.

What's the difference between Pirates, Privateers, & Buccaneers?

Pirates acted on their own, while Privateers acted with the agreement of at least one government. A group of outlaw pirates survived in the West Indies by cooking wild pig on sticks (buccan) and this is how they became known as buccaneers.

 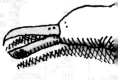

Barbarossa (Red Beard) was Turkish and an admiral of the Ottoman navy. He was very fierce and took control of the western Mediterranean while attacking the Spanish. He captured Algeria and made himself ruler, before handing it as a prize to the Ottoman emperor, who in return gave him two jewel encrusted swords.

Jack 'Calico' Rackham was an English pirate who was famous for pirating in the West Indies and also for designing his 'Jolly Roger' flag. This was a skull and crossed swords. He was eventually captured by the pirate hunter, Jonathan Barnet, in Jamaica. Rackham and most of his crew were hanged.

Captain Kidd was a Scotsman and not so much a pirate as a privateer and pirate hunter. He captured a number of pirate ships and in doing so made himself very unpopular with the East India Company, whose goods were often those he gained. He was hanged as a pirate in London after a trial which some say was a 'fix' involving the East India Company.

Long John Silver was a fictional pirate from Treasure Island. With his one leg and parrot on his shoulder, he is probably the most famous pirate of all. The typical 'pirate voice' (oooh arrgh) was based on the performance of the actor Robert Newton, who played Long John Silver in a movie.

Lady Mary Killigrew was an English 'lady' from Cornwall. She was said to have robbed a Spanish ship while it was in port and its officers were her guests. When they discovered their loss, the officers went to London to complain. Lady Killigrew was given a pardon when her son, a judge, 'interfered' with the investigation.

Charlotte de Berry was first recorded in a 'Penny Dreadful' magazine in 1836. It was said she disguised herself as a male pirate so she could travel with her husband, but he was killed and she was made to marry an officer who she hated and later killed. She was then captured by a captain, who took her as a wife but she killed him too and took his ship. Apparently.

Pirate Bling

Shark's teeth

Rings - bling, bling!

On board ship we wear simple clothes and shoes. But get us on land and it's a different story! We love to show off our fancy clothes. There's no point doing all that swashbuckling (theft some people call it) if we can't look good!

Hats are often part of a pirate's best outfits. We 'collect' them on our voyages, ahem.

Ostrich feathers make splendid decorations for hats.

We like to wear seashells as decorations.

Wearing bright colours used to be against the law - imagine that! Which is exactly why we like to wear them. We often steal rich fabrics and spicy perfumes from merchant ships. Hah!
So much for the rules.

THE MEANING OF PIRATE TATTOOS

a nautical star is for protection and guidance

a swallow for always returning home

an anchor shows an Atlantic crossing

a sparrow is for 5000 miles travelled

a rope around the wrist is to show a deckhand

ship's lamps for Port (left side) and Starboard (right side)

a turtle for crossing the Equator

a ship in full sail shows a trip around Cape Horn

the rooster and pig bring safety, ham, eggs and luck in a fight

EARRINGS
1. Stop seasickness

2. Store wax to plug ears during cannon fire

3. Can be used to pay for a pirate funeral

This Yap stone money is just too heavy!

Sometimes we do embroidery to fancy up our clothes.

Buckles

Silver breastplate

African trading beads

Walrus tooth scrimshaw

Stolen crucifix

Gold doubloon

We pirates like to wear coins and other types of money as well as souvenirs from our voyages as part of our best outfits.

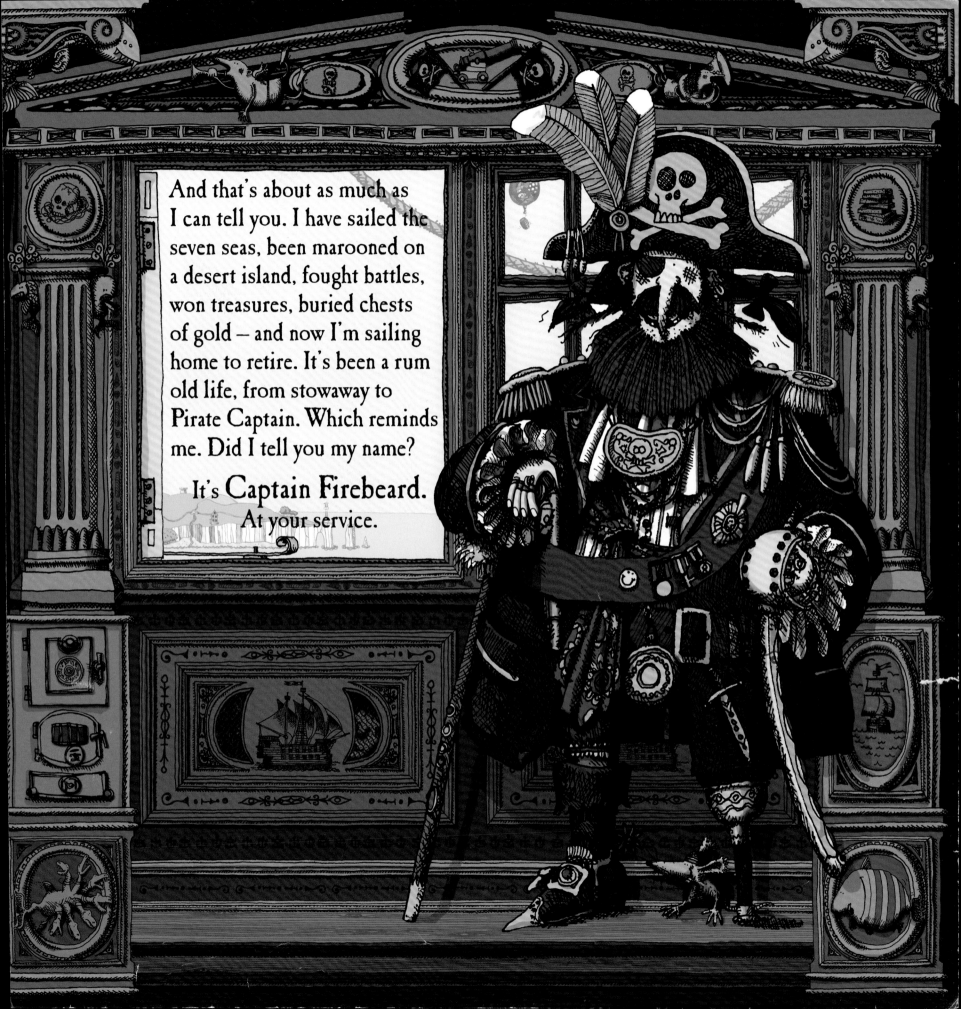

And that's about as much as I can tell you. I have sailed the seven seas, been marooned on a desert island, fought battles, won treasures, buried chests of gold – and now I'm sailing home to retire. It's been a rum old life, from stowaway to Pirate Captain. Which reminds me. Did I tell you my name?

It's Captain Firebeard.

At your service.

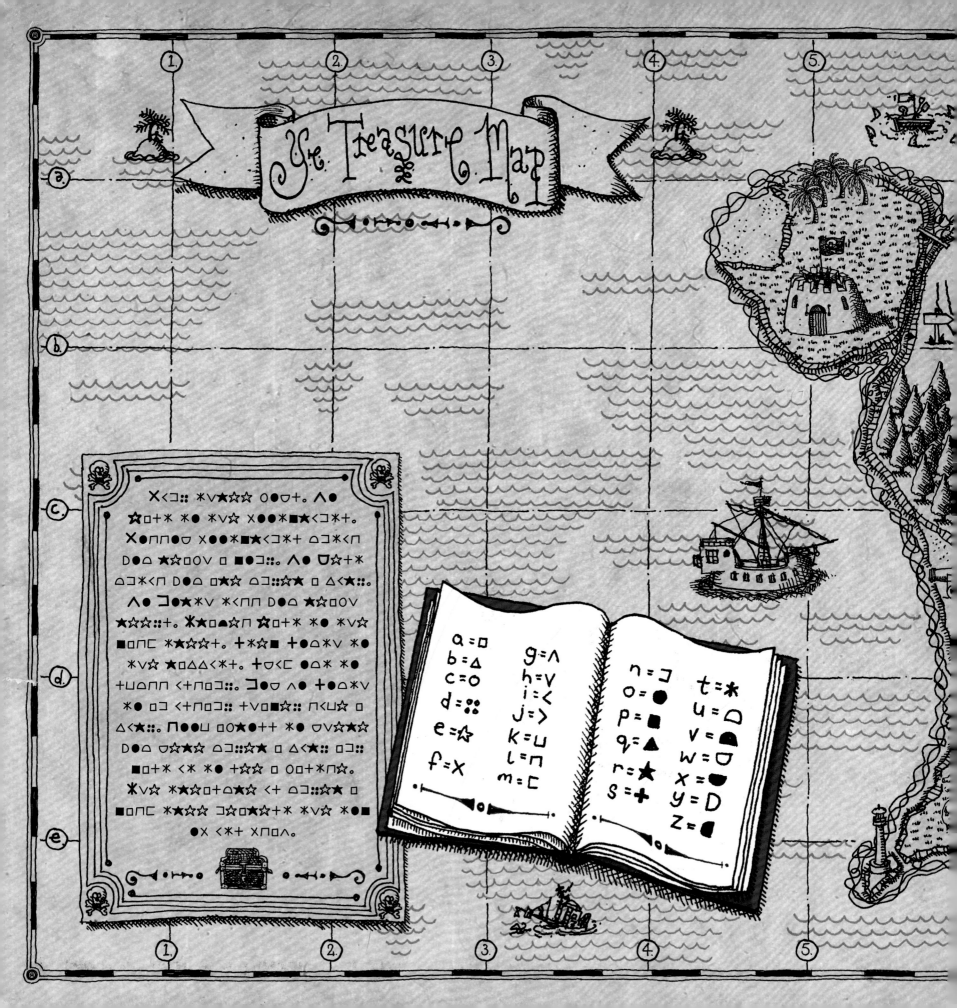